SHERLOCK BONES

AND THE

NATURAL HISTORY MYSTERY

SHERLOCK BONES

AND THE
NATURAL HISTORY
MYSTERY

RENÉE TREML

ALLEN&UNWIN
SYDNEY·MELBOURNE·AUCKLAND·LONDON

STATE NATURAL

Find your Culture

SEE THE WORLD'S LARGEST GEMSTONE

THE ROYAL BLUE DIAMOND

ROAR

Dedicated to my writing partner in crime, Amanda, who has been on Sherlock Bones' journey almost as long as I have.

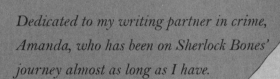

HISTORY MUSEUM

with our DINOSAURS

EXPERIENCE THE RAINFOREST

MINI-BEASTS

BIODIVERSITY

Black Flying-Fox
Pteropus alecto
Australia & Indo-Pacific
Frugivore & Nectarivore
Mammal

Eastern Grey Kangaroo
Macropus giganteus
Australia
Herbivore
Marsupial

Plains Zebra
Equus quagga
Africa
Herbivore
Mammal

Platypus
Ornithorhynchus anatinus
Australia
Carnivore
Monotreme

Numbat
Myrmecobius fasciatus
Australia
Insectivore
Marsupial

Nile Crocodile
Crocodylus niloticus
Africa
Carnivore
Reptile

Oh, hello there!

I'm a frogmouth skeleton on exhibit here at the State Natural History Museum.

WHAT? You've never been to this museum before? Sit back and I'll give you a quick tour.

This doesn't seem right...

Who designed this thing?

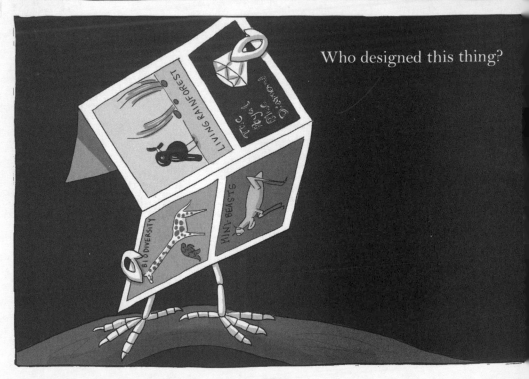

OK, I think I've
got it now.

Come here and
have a look.

You're going to need to get closer than that.

I don't bite.

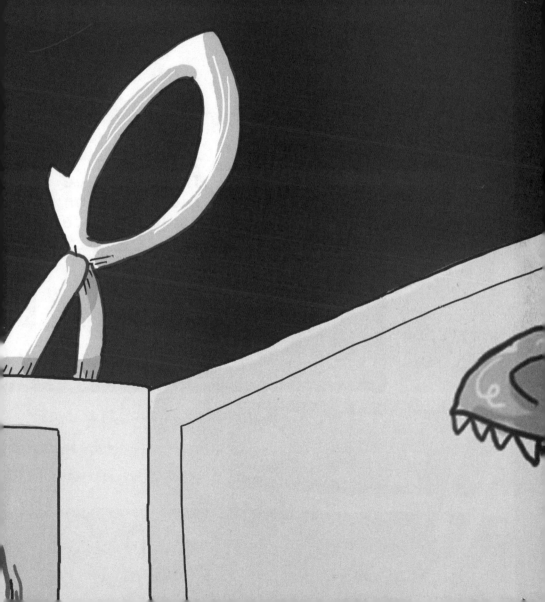

Experience
Australia's Rainforest
Find the elusive frogmouth and come face-to-face with a bowerbird
Our Culture Our World
Share your world in this hands on exhibit
Living Rainforest
Cool human stuff in here, if you're into that sort of thing.
Our Culture Our World
Explore the world's oceans from top to bottom
We have real live butterflies too – so pretty!
There is a giant squid in here, but don't worry, it's dead.
Butterfly Garden
Ocean Life
Creepy, crawly, and
Lobby Info Shop
Mini-beasts
Tarantulas give me the creeps.
Open D
9–5pm
Beautiful, rare and endangered
Visit the Butterfly Garden

To be honest,
I wasn't expecting to
see you until page 34.

That's where all the fun
begins.

But since you are
already here...

Allow me to
introduce myself.

I AM
SHERLOCK
BONES...

...the mystery-solving

SUPERSTAR

of
this
book!

Oh, right.
SORRY, WATTS.

I *totally* meant to
say 'WE'.

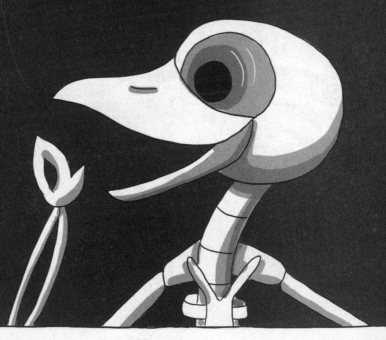

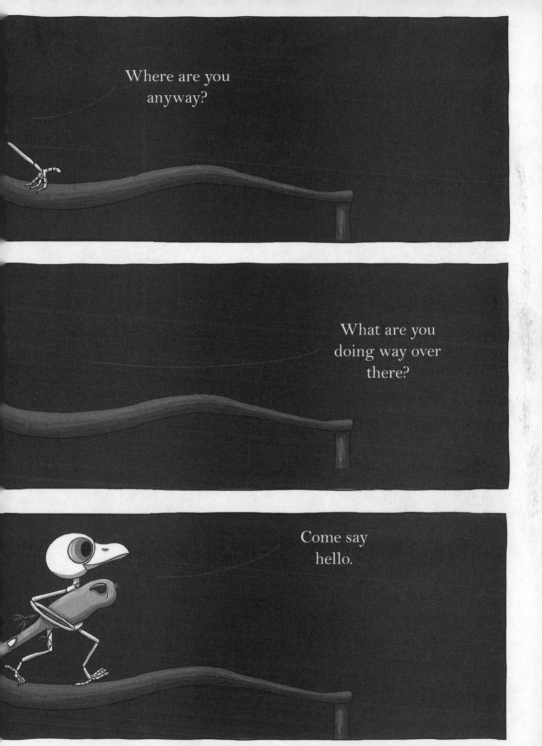

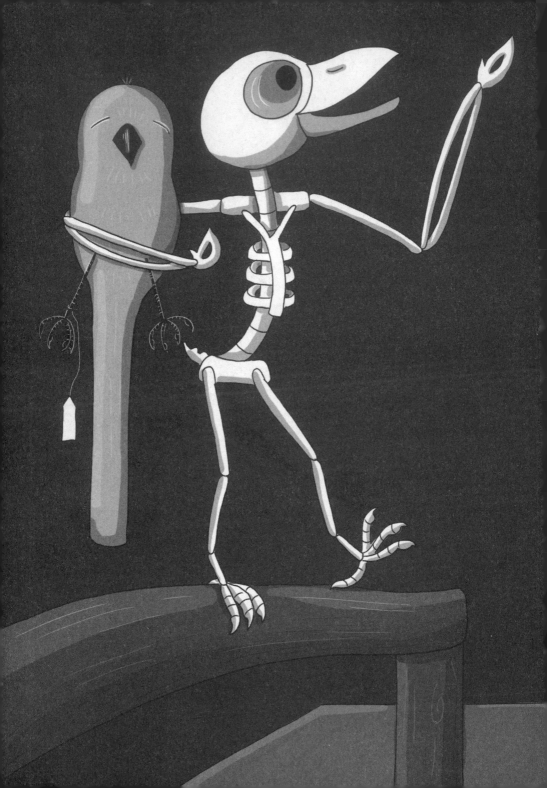

This is my trusty partner Watts,

and together

WE are...

...mystery-
solving

SUPERSTARS!

Tell them that funny joke you told me earlier.

24

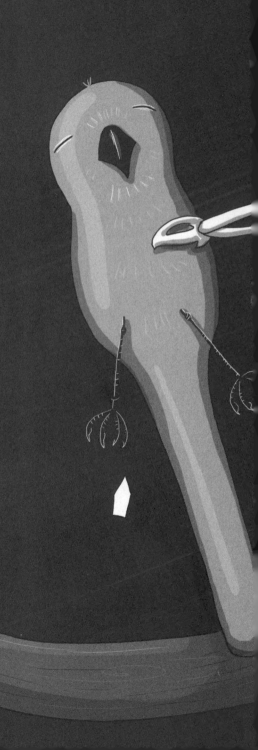

WAIT! NO!!
I'm just introducing me and
Watts — the mystery solvers.

We all
know you
couldn't
solve a
mystery
without me.

You
aren't
exactly
vital
to the
operation.

I am
totally
vital to
the...

OOPS.

Tawny Frogmouth
Podargus strigoides
Australia
Carnivore
Bird

Maybe it's best if you flip
ahead to page 34 now.

That's where the story
starts.

Just skip the next page.
Don't look down.

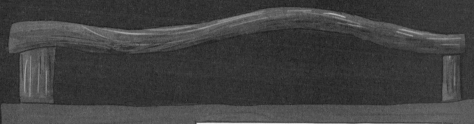

Tawny Frogmouth

Podargus strigoides
Australia
Carnivore
Bird

Ahh ... this is better than that
BEAD-MASSAGE-THINGY
on the Museum Director's chair.
You really should try it, Bones.
It's very relaxing.

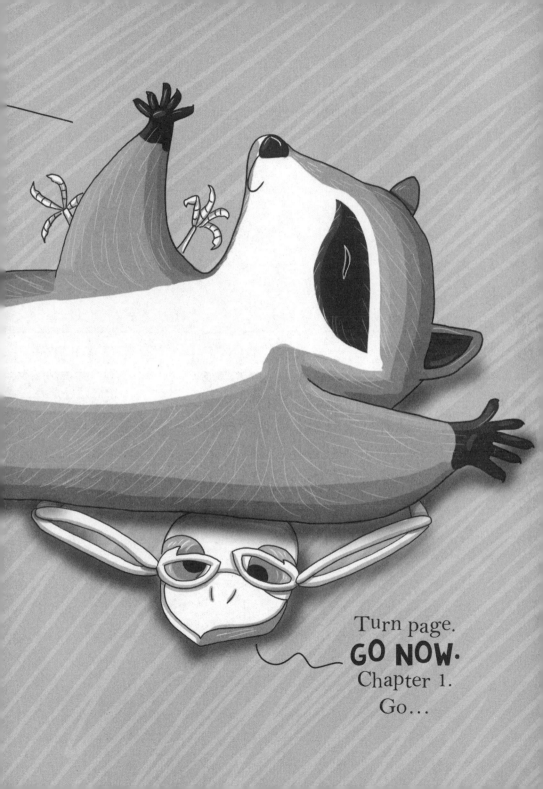

Turn page.
GO NOW.
Chapter 1.
Go…

CHAPTER I
Closing Time

Weeeooo weeeooo Weeeooo weeeooo weeeooo We

STATE NATURAL

Find your Culture

SEE THE WORLD'S LARGEST GEMSTONE

THE ROYAL BLUE DIAMOND

ROAR

Police

Police

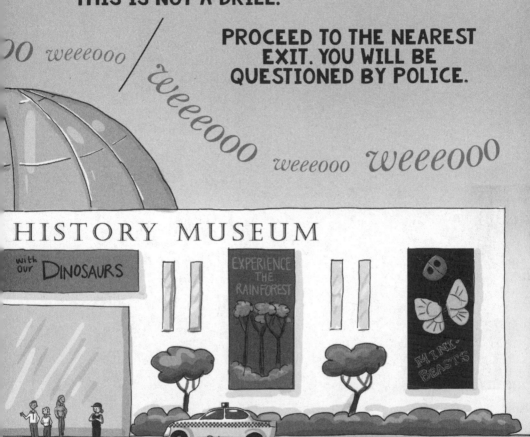

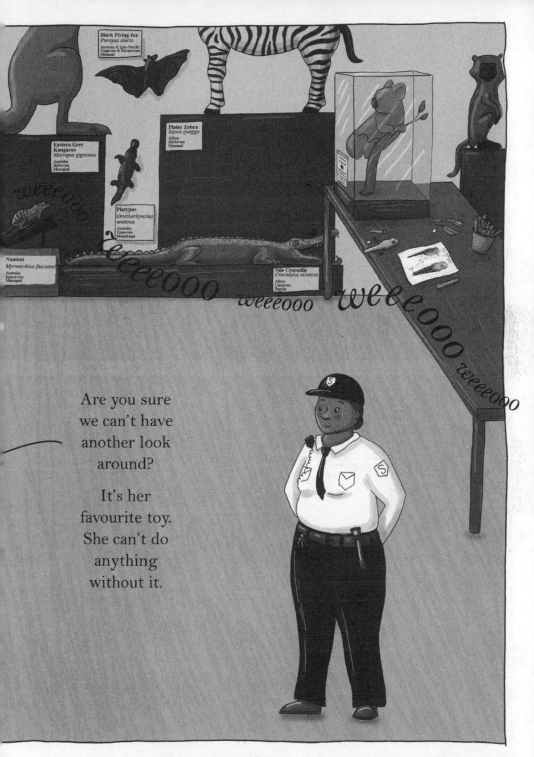

Are you sure we can't have another look around?

It's her favourite toy. She can't do anything without it.

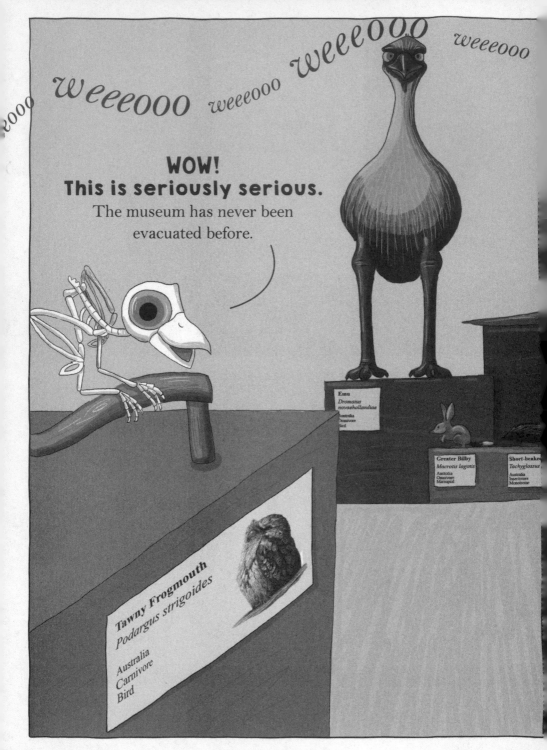

THE WORLD'S MOST VALUABLE GEMSTONE IS MISSING AND THE PRIME SUSPECT IS A GHOST.

That could **shut down** this museum.

Speaking of shutting things down, will you get the lights?

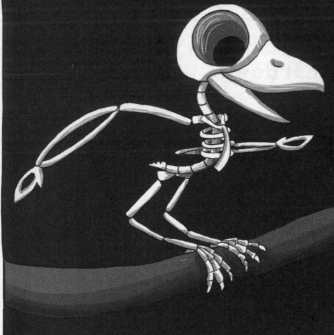

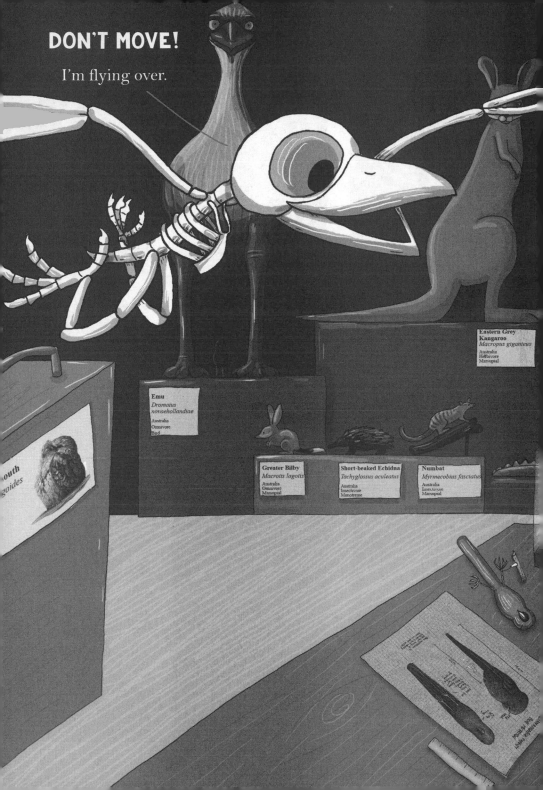

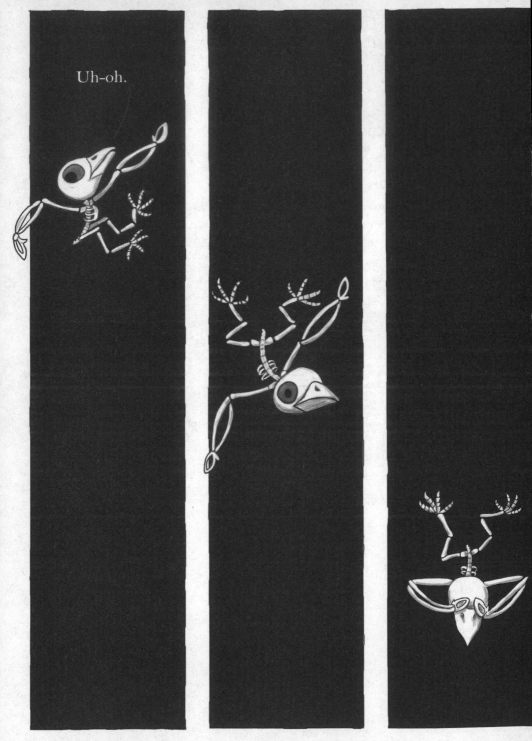

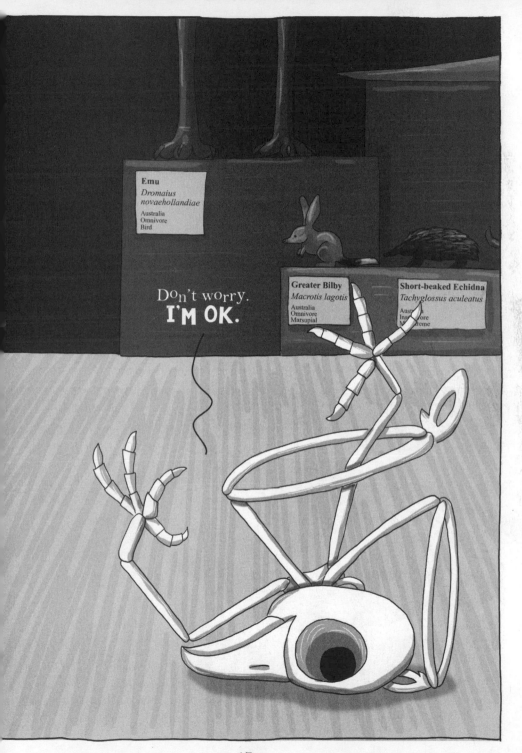

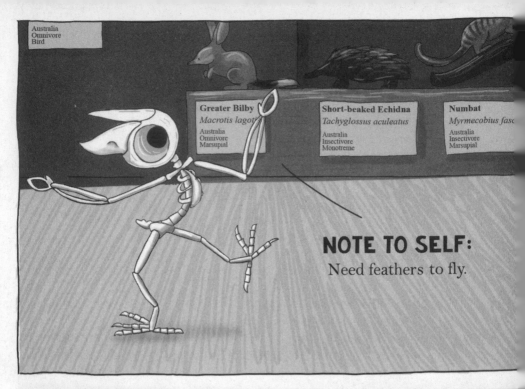

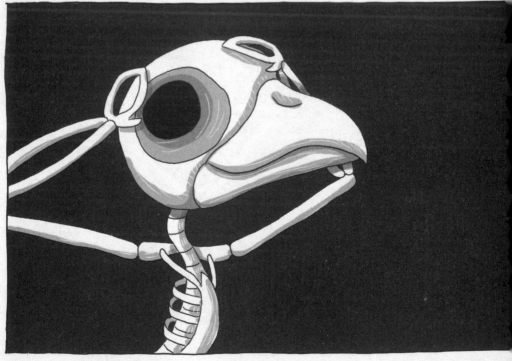

48

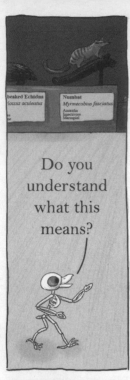

Do you understand what this means?

The museum is going to close!

All because the world's **MOST VALUABLE GEMSTONE** mysteriously disappeared and nobody saw a thing!?

It kind of makes sense when I put it tha way...

So, Watts, I hate to be the one to break it to you...

... but when the museum closes, we will be put in storage!

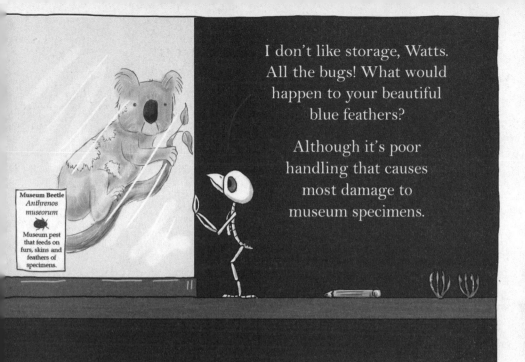

I don't like storage, Watts. All the bugs! What would happen to your beautiful blue feathers?

Although it's poor handling that causes most damage to museum specimens.

Museum Beetle
Anthrenos museorum

Museum pest that feeds on furs, skins and feathers of specimens.

I hope we get a really good packer.

But regardless, we would still be together, right, Watts?

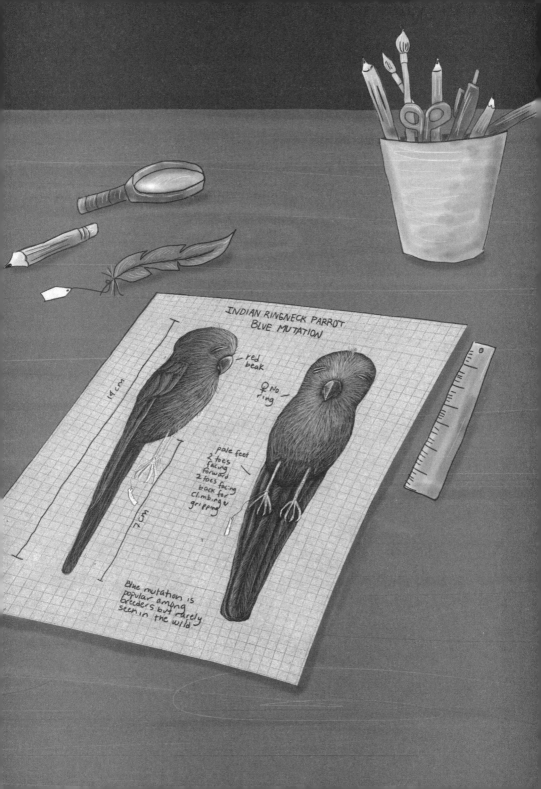

INDIAN RINGNECK PARROT
BLUE MUTATION

red
beak

♀ No
ring

14 cm

7 cm

pale feet
2 toes
facing
forward
2 toes facing
back for
climbing &
gripping

Blue mutation is
popular among
breeders but rarely
seen in the wild.

CHAPTER 2
A Bit of Fluff

Well, how-dee-do and nice to meet you.

I'm Grace.

I'm not from around here.

In fact, I don't even know where I am, but it is so great to have somebody to talk to.

Ya'll need a
REAL
friend.

You know, a
**WALKING,
TALKING,
BREATHING**
friend.
And today is
**your
lucky
day,**
because
**HERE
I
AM.**

Nah. Forget it.
I was only joking.

I didn't want to hang out with you
DEADBEATS anyway.

Now, if ya'll will
excuse me, I've really
got to be going.

Wait! Do you know anything about the Royal Blue Diamond?

Oooh, the big shiny one?

Of course it's **shiny!** It's also **missing!** It was stolen today!

Gee, that's too bad. We raccoons have a soft spot for shiny pretty things.

What's that, Watts?

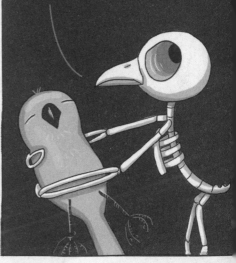

No, I am not being distracted by her flattery. That's exactly what I was going to say before you interrupted me.

This isn't a laughing matter, Grace. The museum is going to close if the diamond isn't found tonight. We have to find the thief!

Here's where I've got to disagree with you,
Sherlock Bones. You see,
WE don't need to do anything.

I on the other hand need chocolate and *I* need it now.
So, stay tuned for the
'Case of the Missing Cocoa'.

Watch it,
Grace!

69

Ha ha!
Good thinking, Watts!
We'll have to remember how much she hates rats the next time we want to get rid of her.

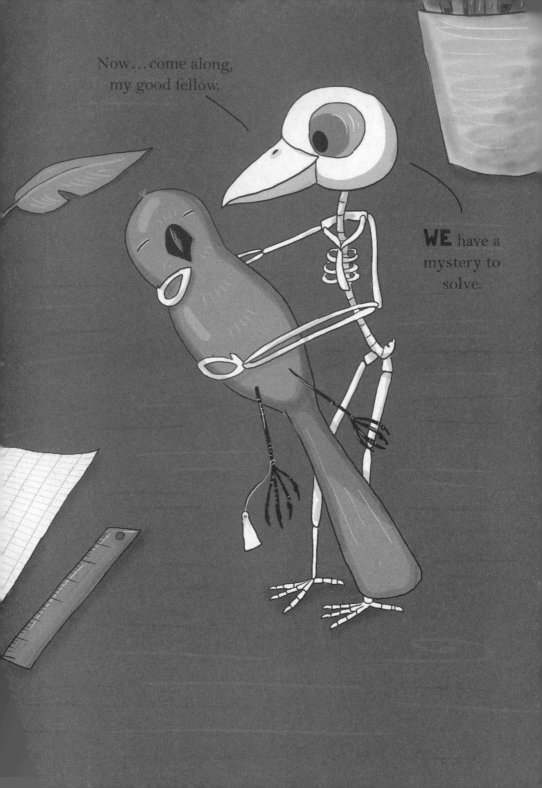

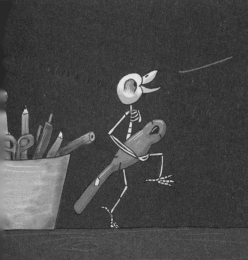

Yes, yes. I know we agreed
NOT to get involved in
museum business again ...

BUT if things keep disappearing, who
knows what will happen to the museum—

—and **US.**

UNLESS...

...they were already in the museum.
Then they wouldn't have to break in at all!

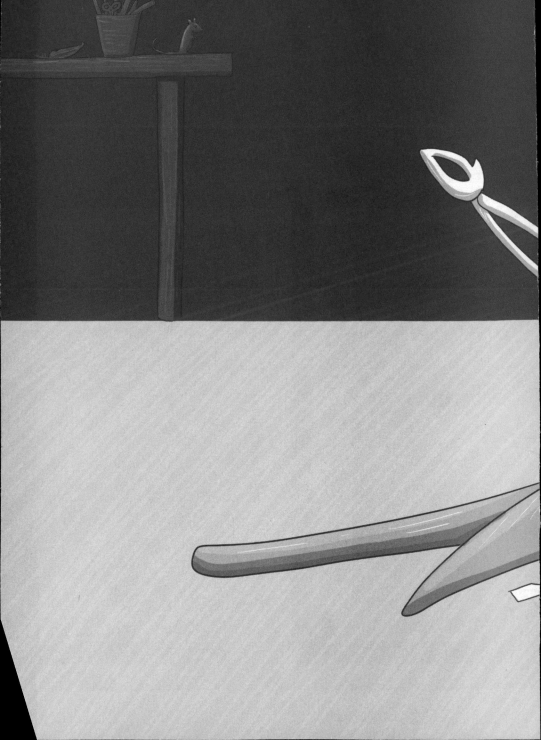

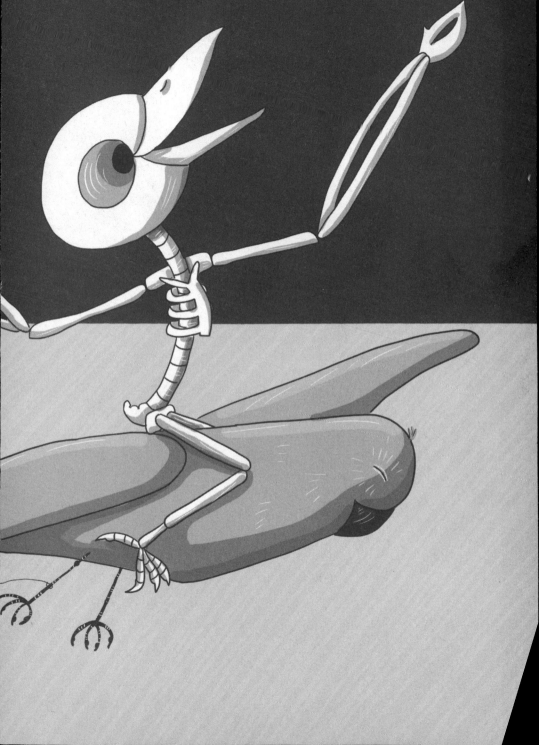

Good point,
Watts.
Let's travel
by foot.

CHAPTER 3
Ghost Stories

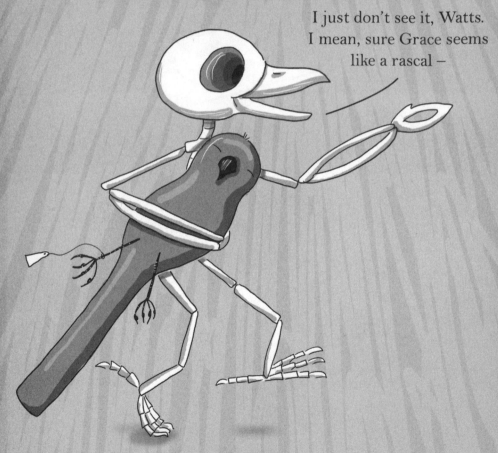

I just don't see it, Watts.
I mean, sure Grace seems
like a rascal –

– and yes, she's
annoying too …

… but she hasn't
stolen anything.

OK, sure.
Have it your way.
She hasn't stolen anything
that we know of
**for certain
YET.**

She just arrived at our museum today.

How could she have stolen the diamond already?

Hmmm ...
you make a good point.

83

It is awfully convenient that she showed up on the *exact same day* the diamond was stolen.

Brown-throated Sloth
Bradypus variegatus

South America
Herbivore
Mammal

Indian Peafowl
Pavo cristatus

South America
Herbivore
Mammal

Scimitar Oryx (juv)
Oryx dammah

Africa
Herbivore
Mammal

Black-faced Impala
Aepyceros melampus

Africa
Herbivore
Mammal

OK, I agree.
We can keep an eye on her…

Herring

Red Her

...even though I don't
think she did it.

85

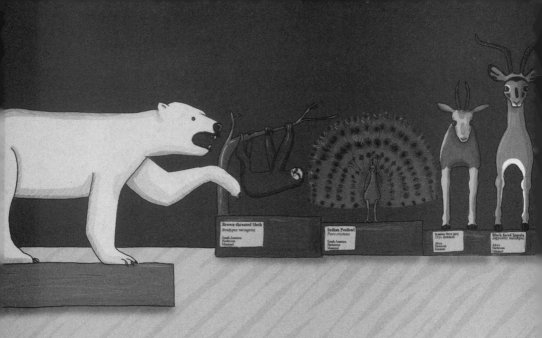

Brown-throated Sloth
Bradypus variegatus

South America
Herbivore
Mammal

Indian Peafowl
Pavo cristatus

South America
Herbivore
Mammal

Scimitar Oryx (pot)
Oryx dammah

Africa
Herbivore
Mammal

Black-faced Impala
Aepyceros melampus

Africa
Herbivore
Mammal

Knobbed Whelk
Busycon carica

Collected: North Carolina, USA

Lightning Whelk
Sinistrofulgur perversum

Collected: North Carolina, USA

Humphrey Wentletrap
Epitonium humphreysii

Collected: Florida, USA

Junonia
Scaphella junonia

Collected: Florida, USA

Banded Tulip
Cinctura lilium

Collected: Florida, USA

Jingle
Jingle

Yes, I have it.

It's right here in
my pocket…

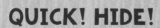

QUICK! HIDE!

*Jingle
Jingle*

Oh no! It must
have fallen out
while I was doing
my rounds.

It could be
anywhere!

Willie Wagtail Nest
Rhipidura leucophrys
Australia

Are you crazy?
Of course, I'm
not going to say
anything to the
police about it.

Jingle
  Jingle

Yes, I know there will
be a lot of trouble
if I don't find it.

Trust me.
I'll find it, OK?

Bye.

Jingle
  Jingle

Willie Wagtail Nest
Rhipidura leucophrys
Australia

Wow.

Did you hear that, Watts?

The security guard stole the diamond!!!

Do you realise that is the security guard we caught sneaking around a few weeks ago?

Yes, I know it's her job to be in the museum at night, but she seems *dodgy*.

OK sure, let's say you are right and she was just looking for the loo …

← RESTROOMS

ROCKS & MINERALS DINOSAURS →

BUT that doesn't explain why she was hanging around in the Rocks and Minerals gallery, where there are no toilets **but there are lots of jewels.**

Dodo
Raphus cucullatus

Mauritius
Last seen 1662

EXTINCT

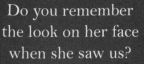

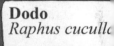

Pepper's Ghost 1860s

Ⓐ clear glass
Ⓑ mirror
Ⓒ real or projected image

How did they do it?
Have a small dark room with a well lit 'ghost'. Reflect the ghost's image into a mirror. The reflection bounces off the clear glass giving a ghostly image.

Ever since that night, she's been going on and on about a little white ghost and how she hears creepy noises at night.

Hmmmm ... maybe she is telling **ghost stories** to distract people from noticing she is the thief!

People believe her. Even the police believe her.

But a GHOST-THIEF?

Seriously, they think that's
a good theory?

Let's just think about this
for a minute.

NUMBER 1:

Why would a ghost steal a diamond?

What would a ghost do with the world's most valuable gemstone anyway?

Buy a haunted house?

Better yet,
NUMBER 2:

How could a ghost steal a diamond?

That diamond is heavy and solid – unlike a ghost.

Even I'd have trouble carrying it and I'm made of good, strong bones.

Ghost Stories from Around the World

Flying Dutchman
Mysterious ghost ship that legend says never made it to port and is forced to sail the oceans forever.

Horse and Carriage
Legends exist worldwide of old-style carriages pulled by ghost horses. Some claim they even leave footprints!

Haunted Hound
Monstrous beast of a spirit dog believed to be a guardian of the afterlife. Similar legends exist in Europe and the Americas.

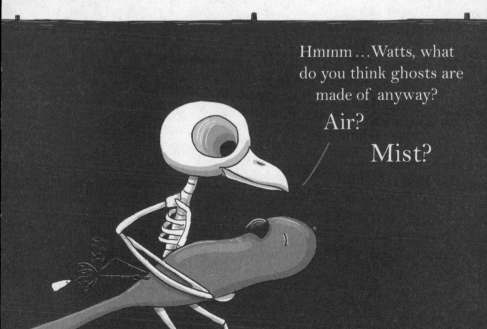

Hmmm...Watts, what do you think ghosts are made of anyway?

Air?

Mist?

Good point, Watts.
That would **TOTALLY** explain why the police are having trouble finding clues.

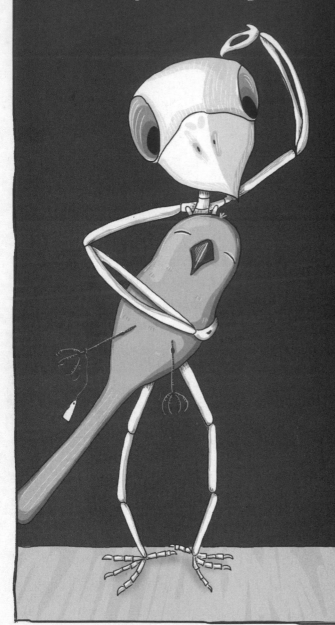

WAIT A MINUTE!

That's not helping!

She thinks WE are the ghosts, remember? And WE didn't steal the diamond!!!

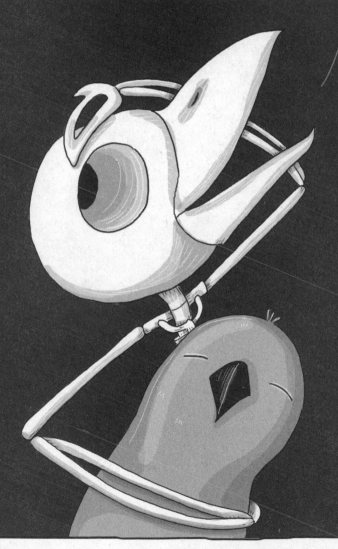

CHAPTER 4
Family Ties

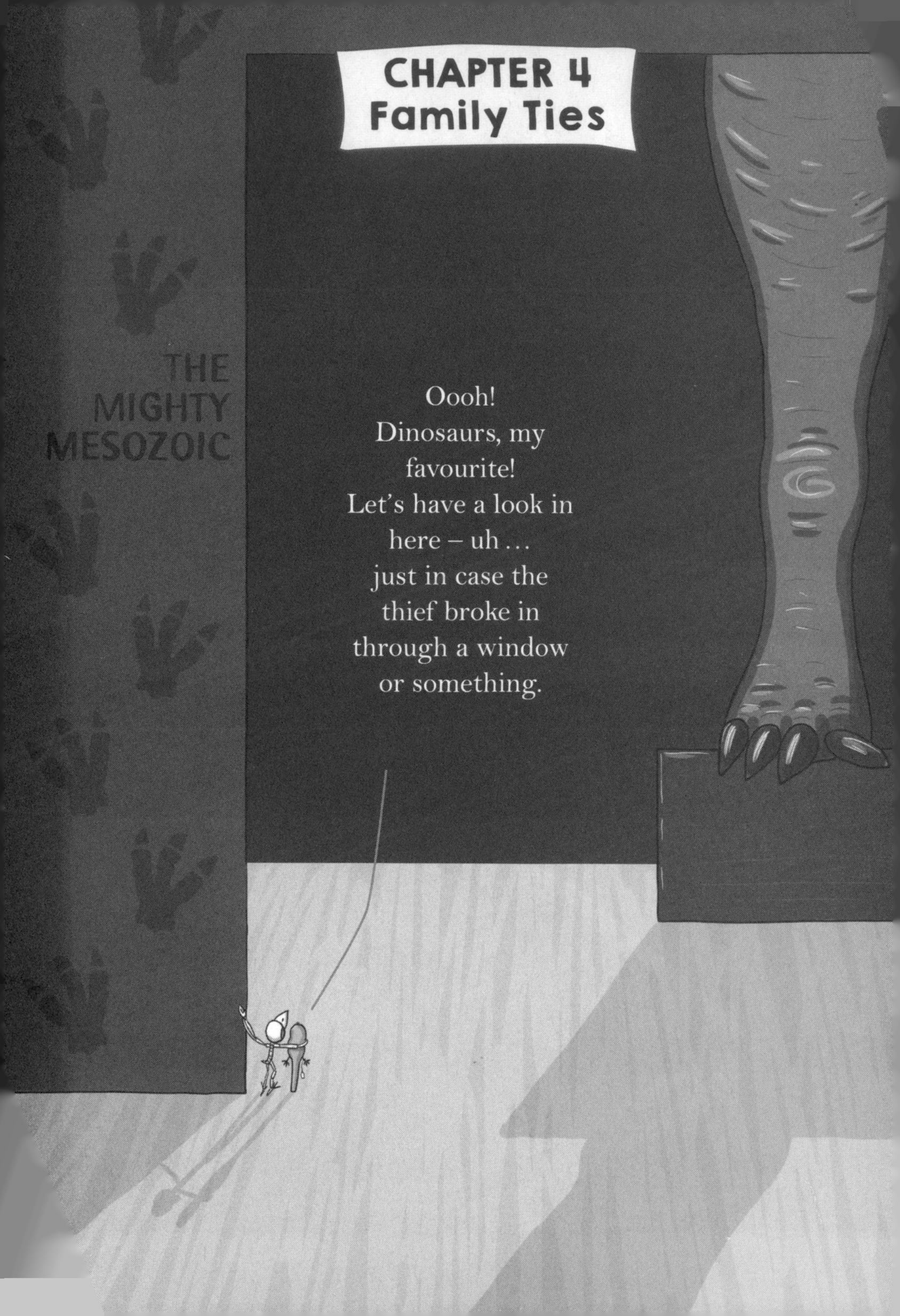

THE
MIGHTY
MESOZOIC

Oooh!
Dinosaurs, my
favourite!
Let's have a look in
here – uh …
just in case the
thief broke in
through a window
or something.

Oh sure, the museum was open at the time so the thief probably walked in through the front door…

…but let's have a look anyway.

We can say g'day to our rellies.

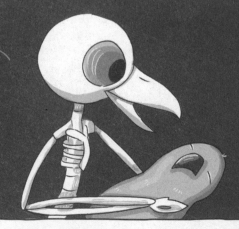

Relatives, Watts.

You know, your accent isn't always so easy to understand either.

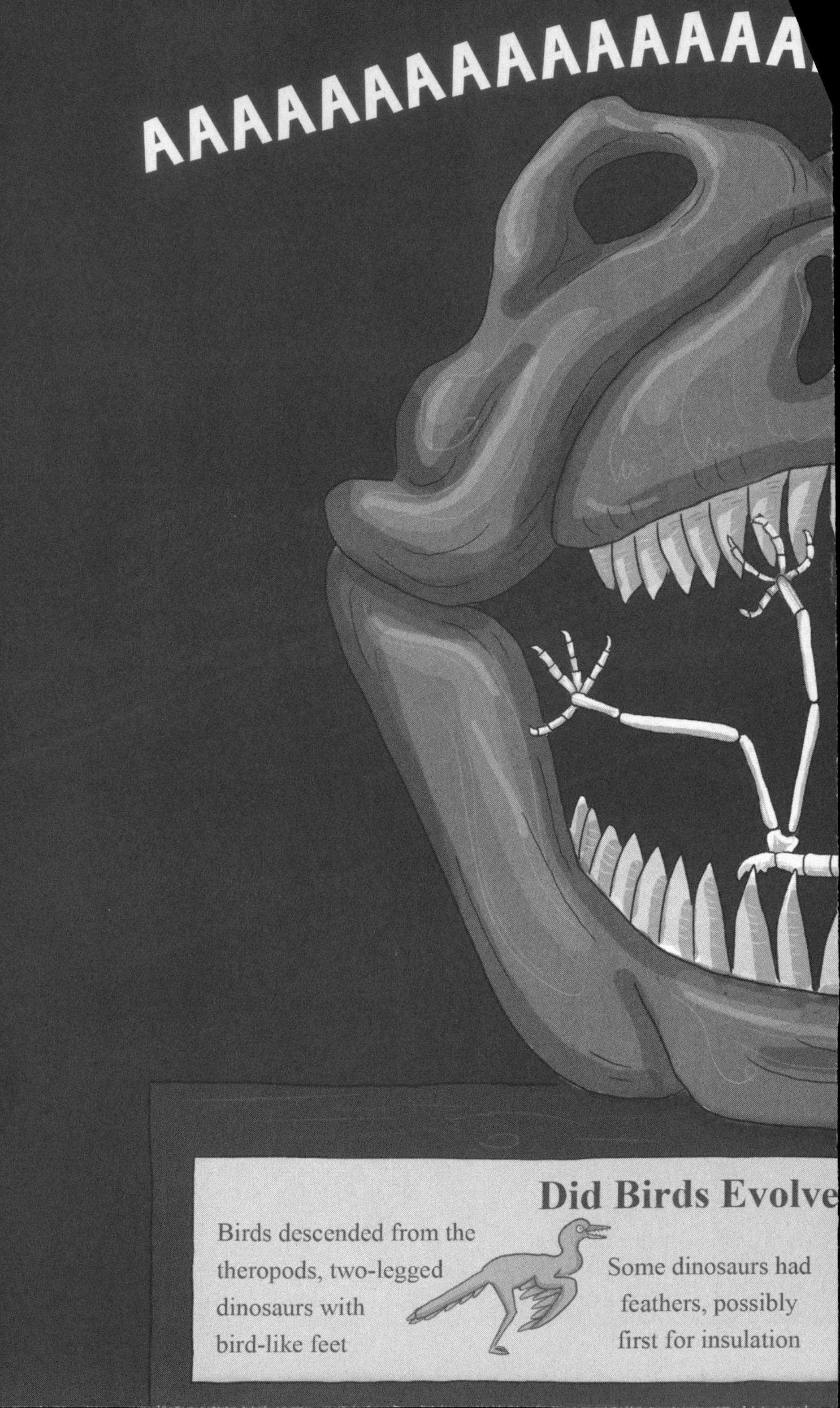

AAAAAAAAAAAAAAAA

Did Birds Evolve

Birds descended from the
theropods, two-legged
dinosaurs with
bird-like feet

Some dinosaurs had
feathers, possibly
first for insulation

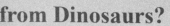
from Dinosaurs?

Dinosaurs shrank drastically in size

Dinosaurs evolved strong breastbones to support flight muscles

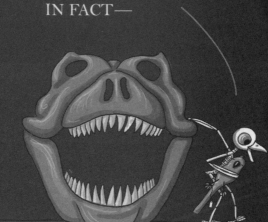

Ha ha!
That always cracks me up, Watts.
You know, we birds are more closely
related to the dinosaur than the lizards.
IN FACT—

Well, look who
it is, **the big
dead bird**
and his
**even
deader
pet.**

Just ignore her, Watts. That's not even a real word.

Excuse us, Grace, we have a thief to catch.

Well, ya'll don't need to look too hard to find one, if you catch my meaning.

Does she mean herself or...

Where did she
come up with
TOODLE-OO???

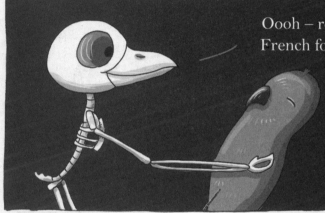

Oooh – really, Watts? It's
French for 'see you later'?

Can you say it
again in French?

You're right.
'À tout à l'heure'
does sound just like
'toodle-oo'.

110

I didn't realise you speak French. I thought you were an **Indian** Ringneck Parrot.

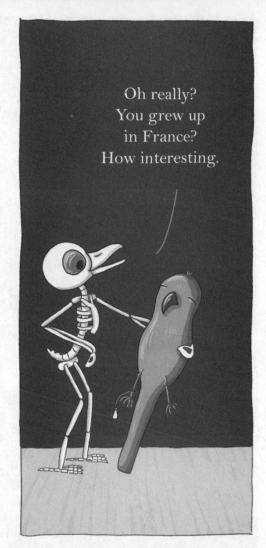

Oh really? You grew up in France? How interesting.

Jingle Jingle

I'd love to see Paris someday. All those bones beneath the city. **So magical.**

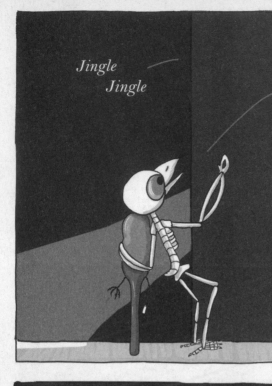

Jingle Jingle

Blimey! I wanted to sneak up on our suspects — not the other way around!

The guard has a volunteer with her. Could he be her partner in crime?

We can catch them red-handed.

You're right! We need a hiding spot for spying.

Good thinking, Watts.
We need a BIRD'S-eye view.

Or in this case, a
DINO'S-eye view
will work perfectly.

Wait here while I check it out.

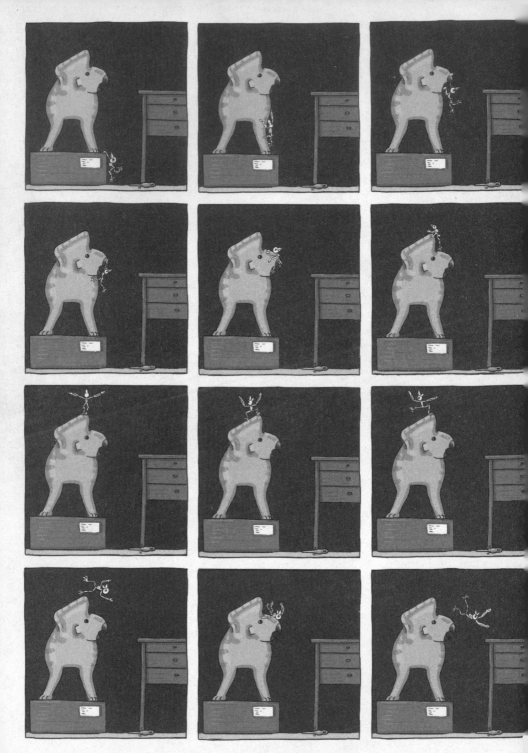

114

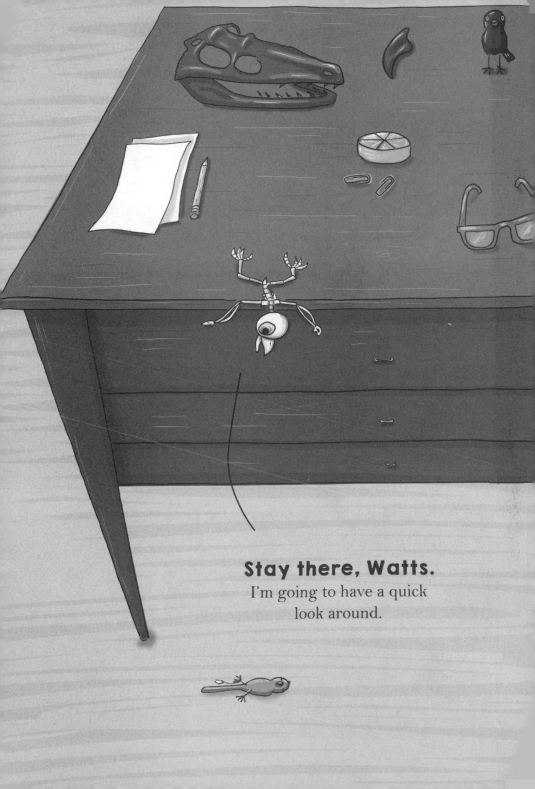

Stay there, Watts.
I'm going to have a quick
look around.

The pencil is always my weapon of choice.

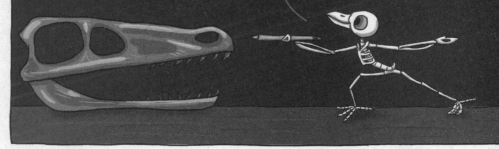

You never know when you'll need to write something underwater or make a note in space...or poke someone in the eye.

On second thought, that's probably not going to help us find the diamond. Unless I draw a new one.

OH, PRETTY!
Wait until Grace sees
these beauties.

Oops.

117

Watts, did you know that the paperclip has remained pretty much unchanged since its invention over 100 years ago?

Yes, I heard what you said about Grace.

I suppose you may be onto something.

She could have stolen the diamond...

...but I just don't see it.

Now, check out all these **fancy colours.** They didn't have paperclips like these in the early 1900s.

Jingle Jingle

Jingle Jingle
Eek!!!
I didn't realise they were so close! We've got nowhere to hide.
Jingle Jingle

So, do you remember where you left your glasses?

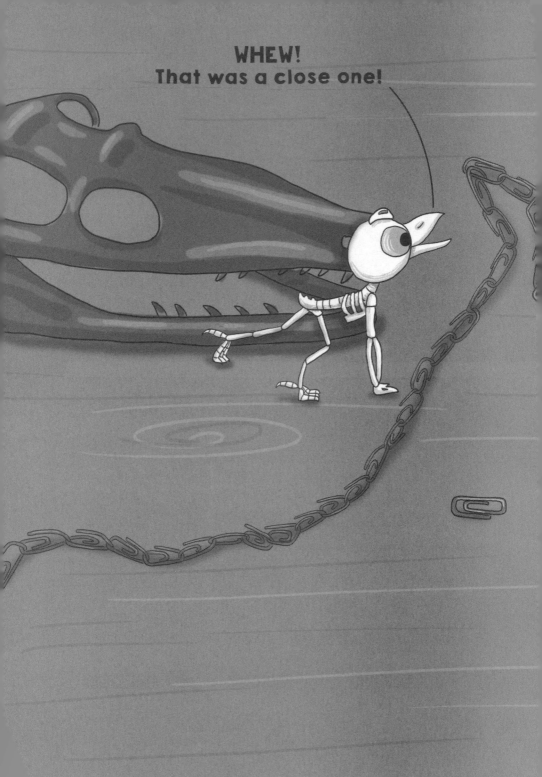

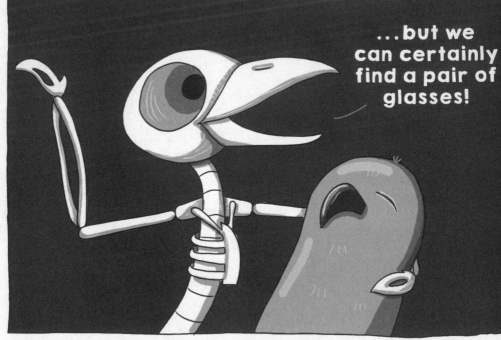

You check over there
and I'll check—

Clatter!

Did you hear that?
MAYBE THERE IS A GHOST!

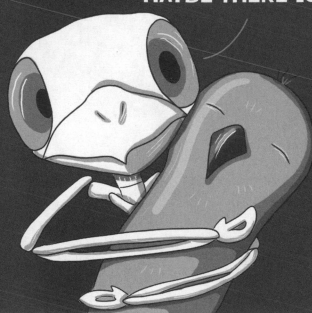

Thump!
Thump!
Thump!

Looking for
something?

Have you heard anything about the DIAMOND, Grace?

Oooh ... I heard that it's **PRETTY and SHINY too.**

I'm guessing you haven't caught the thief yet? You and your little pet are totally **clue-less...**

... but maybe you can solve this mystery, Sherlock Bones.

Toodle-oo!

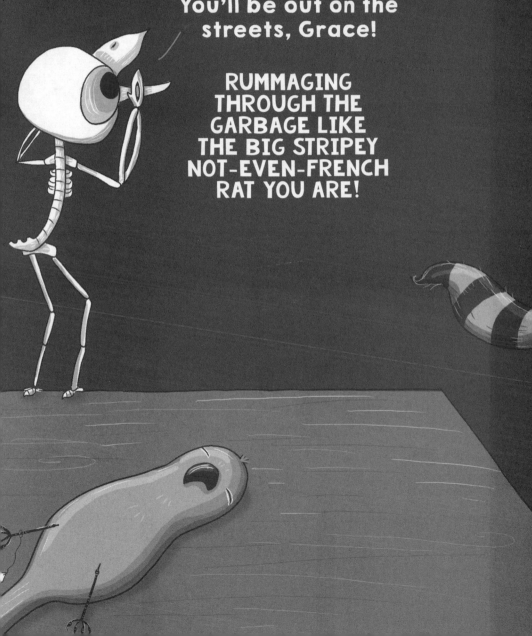

Hey! I knew you stole the glasses all along!

Do you know what will happen
if the diamond isn't found?

**You'll be out on the
streets, Grace!**

**RUMMAGING
THROUGH THE
GARBAGE LIKE
THE BIG STRIPEY
NOT-EVEN-FRENCH
RAT YOU ARE!**

Do you really think Grace would be able to put the diamond down for **one teeny tiny little second** if she already had it in her **sticky paws?**

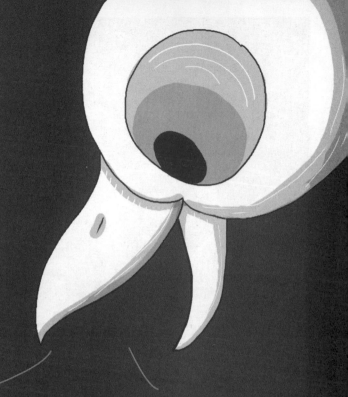

My point exactly.
Grace doesn't have the diamond.
At least not yet.

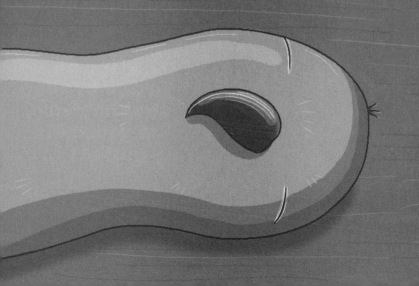

On the other hand,
the security guard
seemed awfully nervous,
didn't you think?
**Highly
suspicious.**

Hmmmm... I suppose she could
be **genuinely afraid of ghosts**...
I mean US.

What if she was afraid that
Mr-Missing-Glasses
would catch her stealing something else?

**After all,
Grace proved
that he really
did lose his
glasses...**

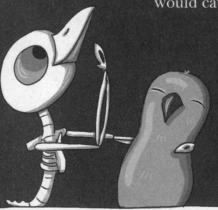

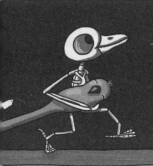

We should keep an eye on that guard.

Yes, yes, of course, Watts, you have a good point.

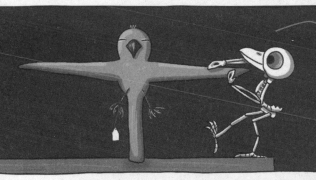

We will check out the **crime scene** first...

...but I bet we don't find any raccoon fur.

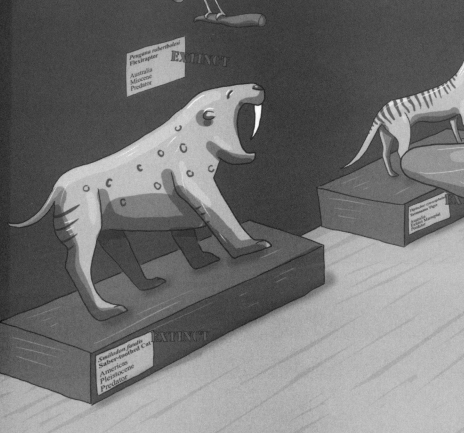

ROCKS & MINERALS

Penguna robertbolesi
Flexiraptor
EXTINCT

Australia
Miocene
Predator

Tilytacinus cynocephalus
Tasmanian Tiger
EXTINCT

Australia
Extinct Marsupial
Predator

Smilodon fatalis
Saber-toothed Cat
EXTINCT

Americas
Pleistocene
Predator

NOW THIS IS FLYING!!!

Like a little
police tape…

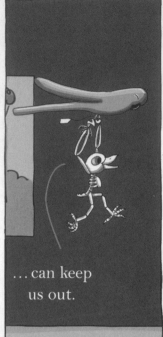

…can keep
us out.

Uh-oh.

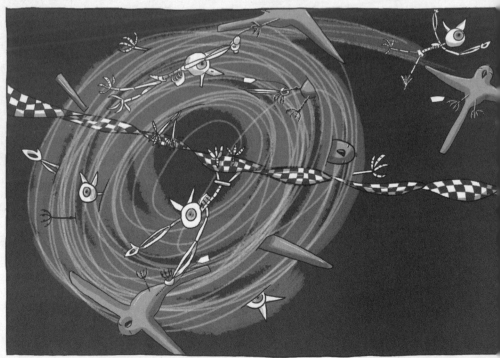

Crash!

Hrmph. I'll be the first to admit that didn't go as planned.

ROYAL BLUE DIAMOND

Jingle Jingle

Jingle Jingle

Wh-who's there?
H-h-hello?

Hey!
She's not supposed
to be in here.
This is a
**protected
crime scene.**

We'd better find
a place to hi—

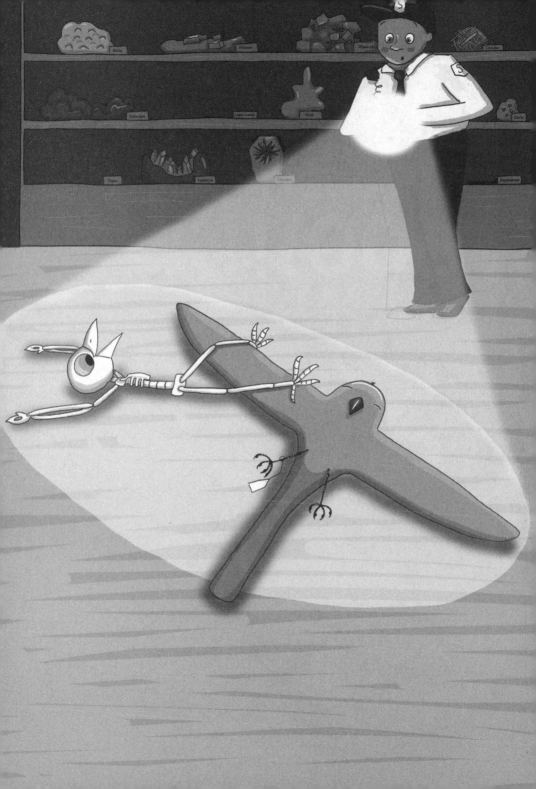

BOOGETY
BOOGETY
BOO!!!

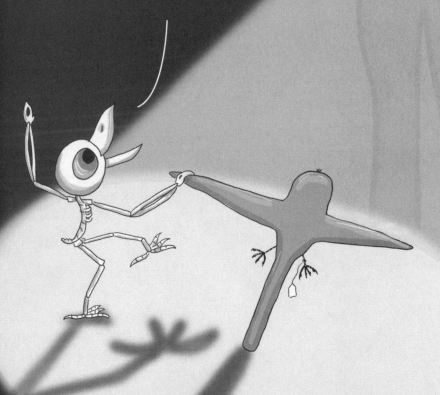

*Jingle
Jingle*

Ha ha ha!
Did you see her face, Watts?
That was even better than
last time!

145

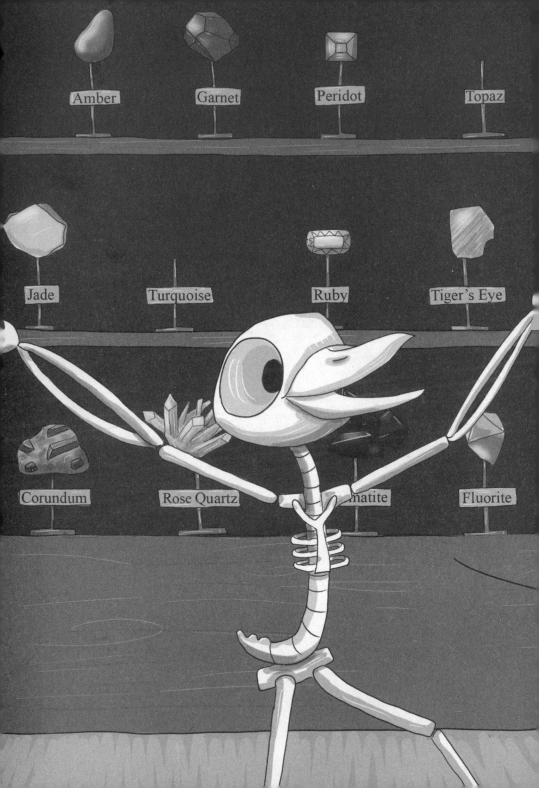

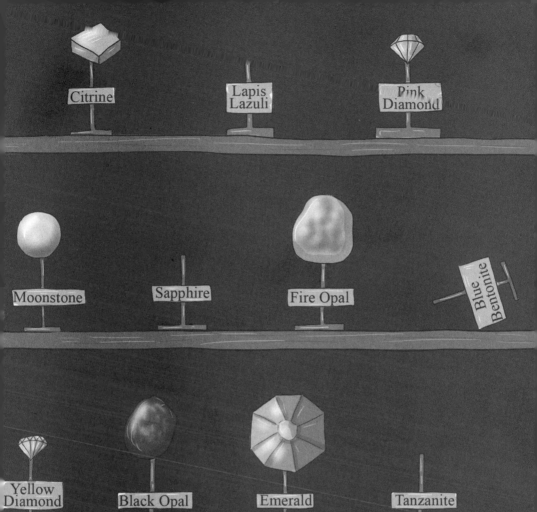

Citrine

Lapis
Lazuli

Pink
Diamond

Moonstone

Sapphire

Fire Opal

Blue
Bentonite

Yellow
Diamond

Black Opal

Emerald

Tanzanite

Anyway, here we are!

The scene of the crime.

The Rocks and Minerals gallery.
Once home to the world's most
valuable diamond!

CHAPTER 6
Sweet Tooth

You are probably right, Watts.

That wasn't the nicest way to handle the security guard...
although you have to admit it was pretty funny!

She's not supposed to be in here anyway.

But we know we aren't suspects, so it's OK for us to be here.

That's a really good question. *I* think the security guard is up to something and *you* think Grace is involved ...

WHOA!

This job is more dangerous than I thought. Now, what was I saying?

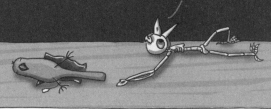

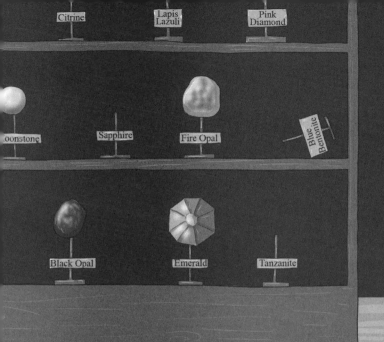

Citrine

Lapis Lazuli

Pink Diamond

oonstone

Sapphire

Fire Opal

Blue Bentonite

Black Opal

Emerald

Tanzanite

That's right – we have
**two highly suspicious
suspects.**

Let's find some clues.

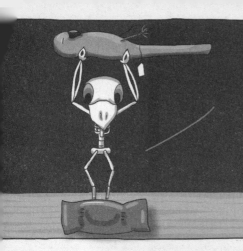

Watts! What kind of
detective are you?
**Are you eating
chocolates at the
scene of the crime?**

You've left quite a mess.

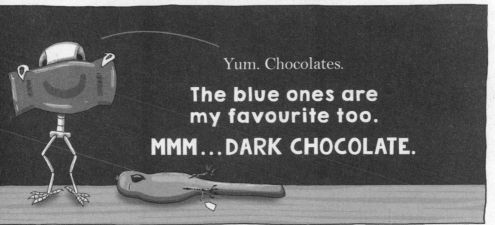

Yum. Chocolates.

**The blue ones are
my favourite too.**

MMM...DARK CHOCOLATE.

The thief must have left
these wrappers.

Great detecting, Watts!

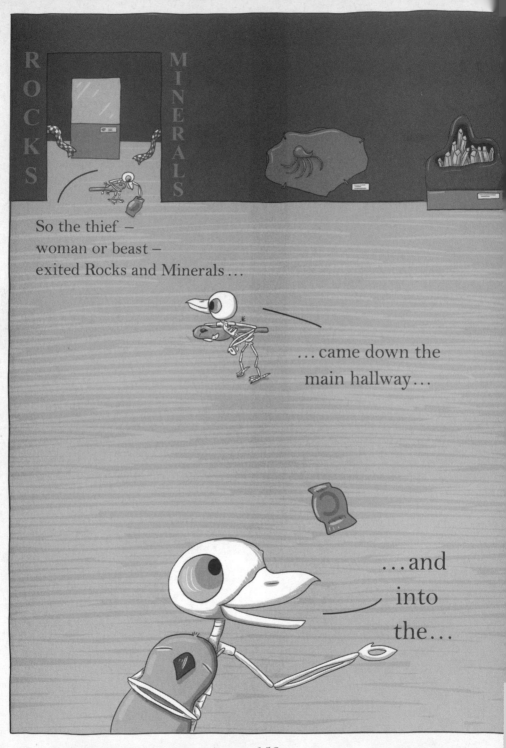

So the thief –
woman or beast –
exited Rocks and Minerals…

…came down the
main hallway…

…and
into
the…

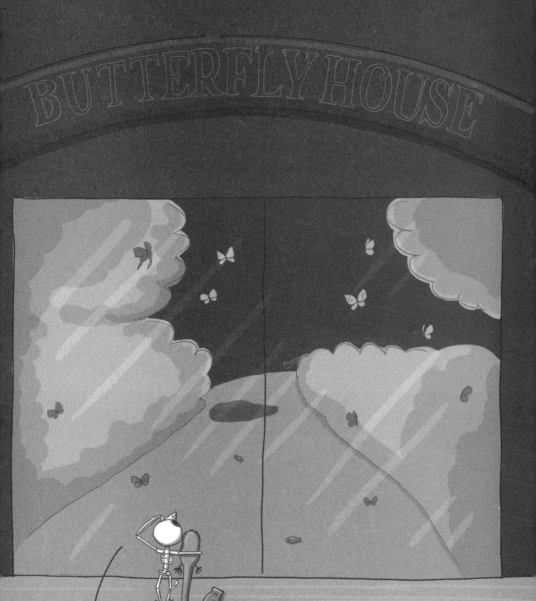

The Butterfly House?
Why would she come in here?

160

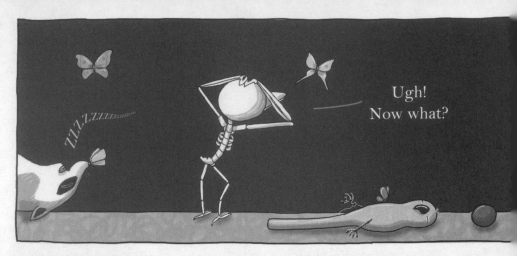

Ugh!
Now what?

Oh, perhaps you
are right, Watts.

Let's just follow the trail
of chocolates.

Hey, Watts, who would
be **crazy** enough
to steal chocolates from
a hungry raccoon?

The Butterfly House is quite a magical place.
Although they really should call it

'The
BUTTERFLY and
MOTH House.'

BUTTERFLY   or   MOTH?

Club-shaped Antennae   **Feathery Antennae**

Resting Wings Up   **Resting Wings Open**

Mostly Diurnal   **Mostly Nocturnal**

Cassia Butterfly *Catopsilia pomona* Small Yellow	**Ulysses Butterfly** *Papilio ulysses* Large Blue and Black	**Cairns Birdwing** *Ornithoptera euphorion* Very Large Green, Yellow and Black	**Atlas Moth** *Attacus wardi* Very Large Brown and white	**Luna Moth** *Actias luna* Large Pale Green	**Emperor Gum Moth** *Opodiphthera eucalypti* Large Light Brown

The moth gets so little attention – although being nocturnal they don't get seen quite as frequently ...

... and some people do find them a bit creepy.

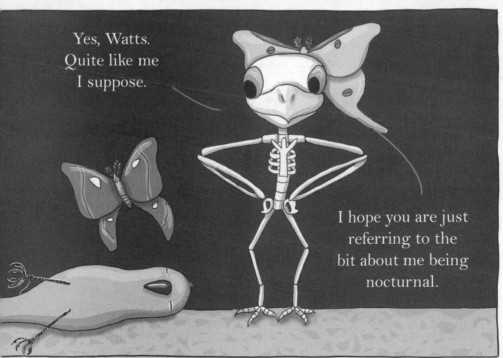

Yes, Watts. Quite like me I suppose.

I hope you are just referring to the bit about me being nocturnal.

Leave it!
That's
evidence.

Welcome to the world of the
MINI-BEASTS

COLOPTERA
Rainbow of Beetles

Did I say the moths
were amazing?

Just look at this
rainbow of beetles!

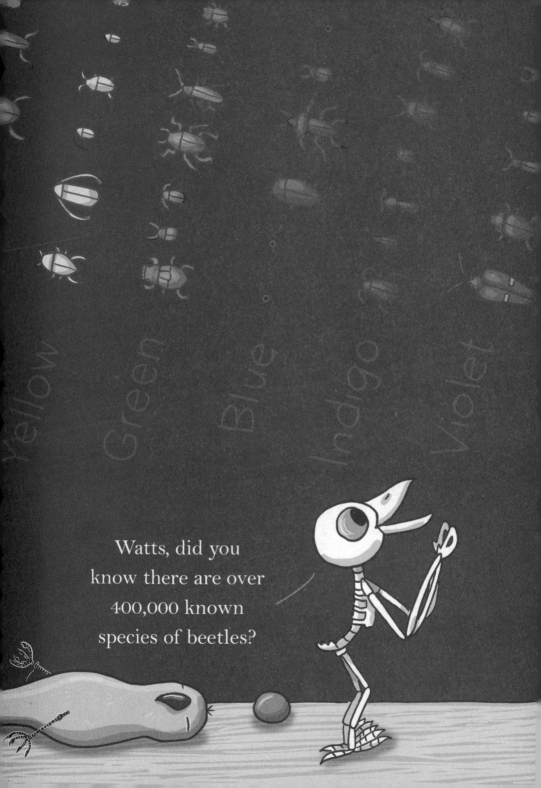

Yellow Green Blue Indigo Violet

Watts, did you
know there are over
400,000 known
species of beetles?

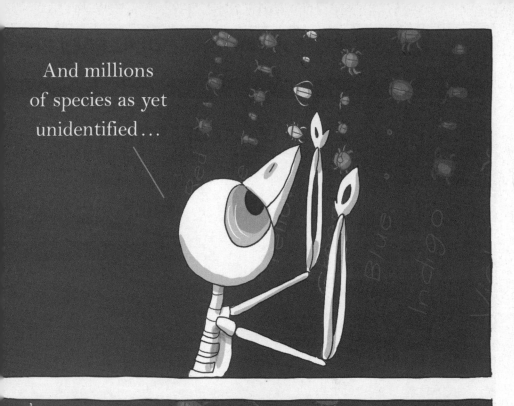

And millions
of species as yet
unidentified...

Not missing, Watts.
Unidentified...
it's totally different.

Beetles are so pretty and shiny.
They look just like little gemstones—

Ceremonial Headdress
Papua New Guinea

Made with feathers, fur and beetles

I've just about had enough of that talking fur coat for one night.

Listen up, Grace. We are trying to solve a mystery here. We don't have time for your shenanigans! Right, Watts?

Uh ... where did you go, Watts? **Watts?**

This isn't funny, Grace!

Give me Watts!

WATTS!
WATTS!

**Which way
did she go?**

OCEAN LIFE

OUR WORLD

BUTTERFLY HOUSE

My dear Watts. Not
only have we not found
the diamond, but now
I've lost you too.

CHOCOLATES
DARK CHOCOLATE

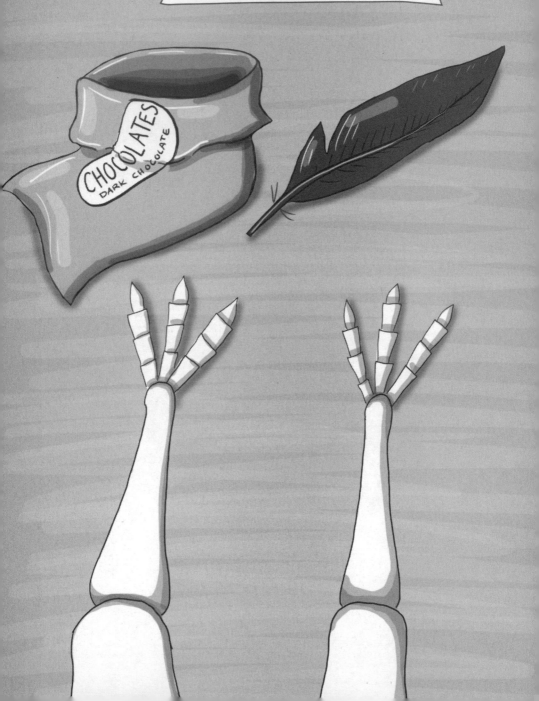

Oh, Watts, you were such a lovely shade of **blue.**

Oh. This feather didn't belong to Watts. It's so dark it's almost black.

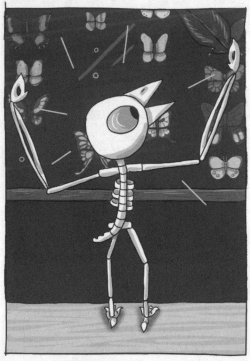

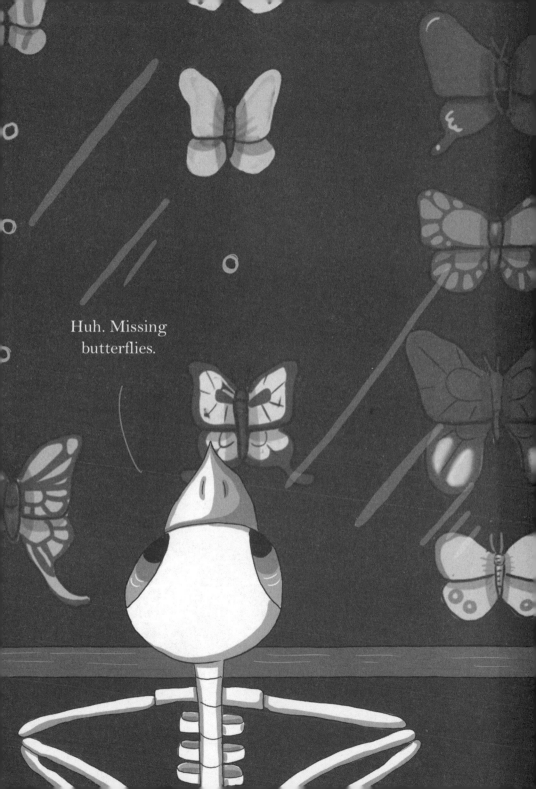

Missing **blue** beetles!

Missing **blue** chocolate wrappers!

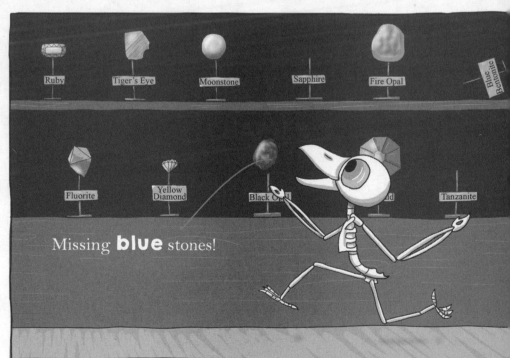

Ruby · Tiger's Eye · Moonstone · Sapphire · Fire Opal · Blue Bentonite

Fluorite · Yellow Diamond · Black Opal · Tanzanite

Missing **blue** stones!

And one blue-black feather.

I'M COMING, WATTS!

LIVING RAINFOREST

I should have known it was a bowerbird. All those blue things. Poor guy, he's just trying to attract a lady.

PUSH TO OPEN

MAPS

Hey! Open up!

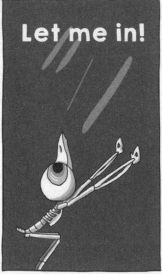

Let me in!

STUPID DOORS!

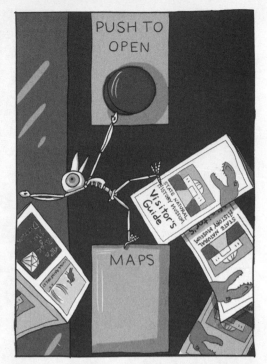

Jingle Jingle

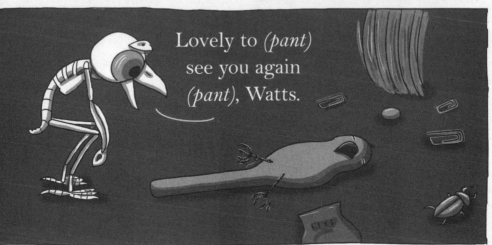

Lovely to *(pant)* see you again *(pant)*, Watts.

Satin Bowerbird
Ptilonorhynchus violaceus

Males: Indigo blue

Females: Olive green with lighter belly
and dark brown markings

Bowerbirds live in wet forests and woodlands. They
eat fruits, leaves and insects. The male bird builds a
bower on the ground using sticks and twigs. He
decorates the ground with blue objects he finds,
hoping to attract a female bowerbird.

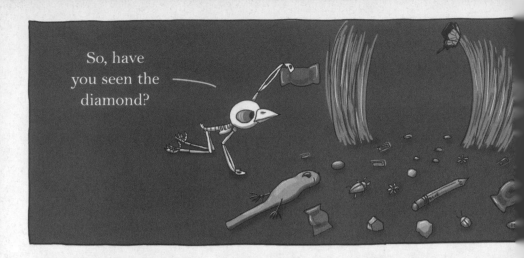

So, have you seen the diamond?

The security guard is coming to steal it from the bowerbird who stole it from the museum.

Look at all this stuff! See, I told you Grace wasn't the thief.

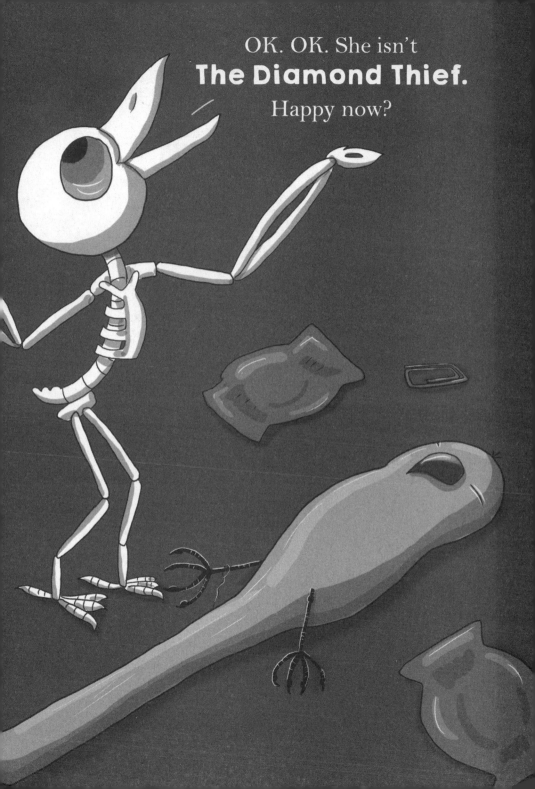

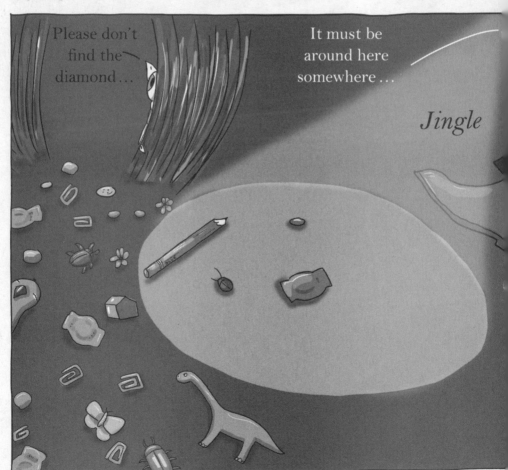

HOORAY!

I've found Nelle's dinosaur!

I finally found it!

You've got to be kidding me. That's what she's been searching for? Shouldn't she be looking for the diamond?

209

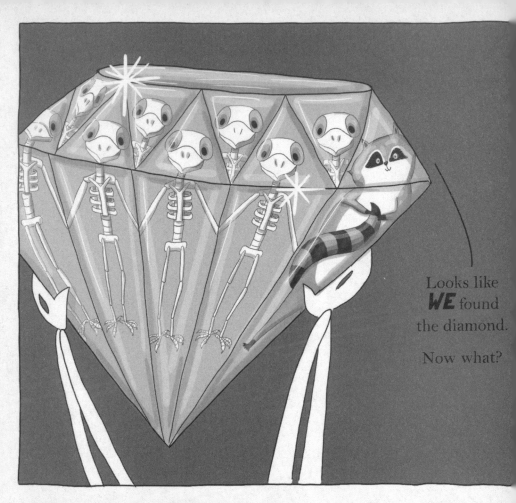

Looks like **WE** found the diamond.

Now what?

Thank goodness you're safe, Grace! Quick, you take the diamond and I'll carry Watts.

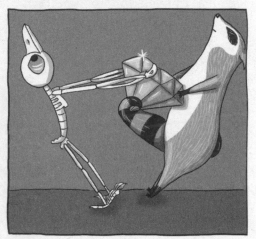

Shhhhhh…
Do you hear that?

Oh phew. It's just a cute little rat.

I mean, a **BIG, FAT, UGLY, HAIRY RAT.**

There are even more rats outside, Grace. The streets are crawling with them.

Pitter-patter

Which is exactly where you will be if the museum closes, Grace. Alone. On the streets with the rats.

Pitter-patter

Are those footsteps? Blimey! I didn't notice that it's morning already. The museum must be open!

We've got to get the diamond to the Director's office pronto.

A little help here, Grace? I can't carry Watts and the diamond by myself.

Pitter-patter

225

COULD THIS SITUATION GET ANY WORSE?

Mandy! Mandy! There's an ALIVE DEAD BIRD!

DON'T TOUCH IT, NELLE!
Is it the bowerbird?
Did he try to eat Bluey?

Come here, little birdie. I won't hurt you.

Oh crikey.
What are we
going to do now?

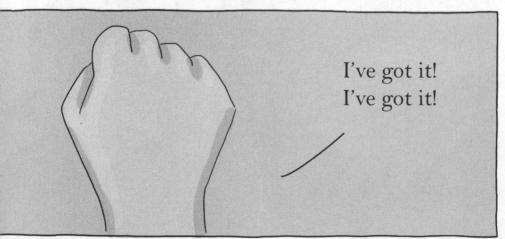

CHAPTER 12
Rest for the Wicked

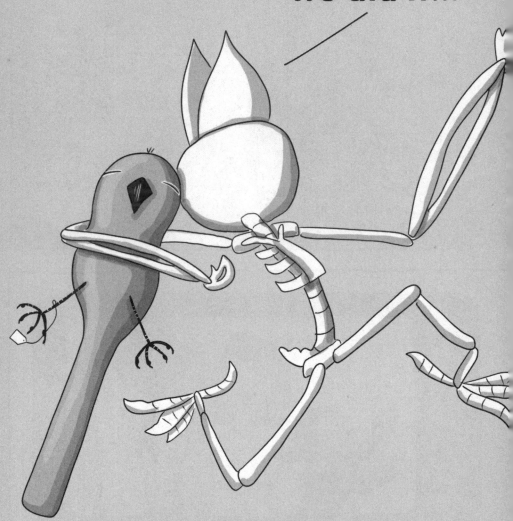

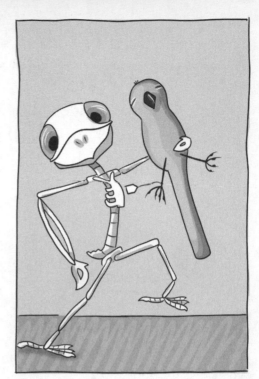

Goodbye?
You've only
just got here.

Plus, we've saved the museum!
It's not going to close.
We can stay here forever.

I'm just another **PEST** to the museum.

We thought so at first too, especially Watts. But I'm sure they will love you once they get to know you!

Pest as in VERMIN. They've called in an exterminator.

Oh. Sorry.

Don't worry.
I'll be fine.

Toodle-oo.

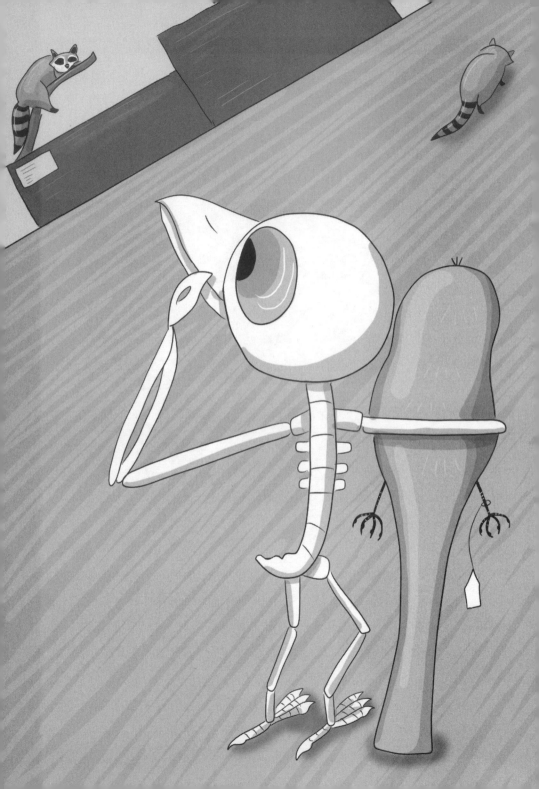

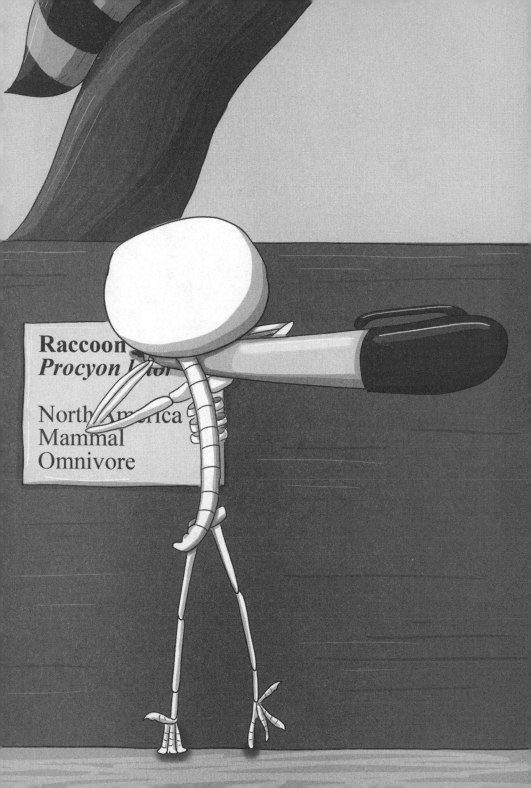

Raccoon $
Procyon lotor

North America
Mammal
Omnivore

y Squirrel
linensis

Eastern Chipmunk
Tamias striatus

North America
Mammal
Omnivore

Aardvark
Orycteropus after
Africa
Carnivore
Mammal

Emu
Dromaius novae
Australia
Omnivore
Bird

Toodle-oo!

First published by Allen & Unwin in 2019

Allen & Unwin
83 Alexander Street
Crows Nest NSW 2065
Australia
Phone: (61 2) 8425 0100
Email: info@allenandunwin.com
Web: www.allenandunwin.com

A catalogue record for this book is available from the National Library of Australia

ISBN 978 1 76052 395 4

For teaching resources, explore www.allenandunwin.com/resources/for-teachers

Cover design by Sandra Nobes
Text design by Renée Treml
Printed in April 2019 in Australia by McPherson's Printing Group

3 5 7 9 10 8 6 4 2

The paper in this book is FSC® certified. FSC® promotes environmentally responsible, socially beneficial and economically viable management of the world's forests.

ACKNOWLEDGEMENTS

I am lucky to belong to the greatest writing group in the world and I owe them so many thanks for all their encouragement and support over the years… and most importantly for never once complaining when I asked them to read *Sherlock Bones* again and again (and again). Thank you to Scott, Alison, Victoria, Vair, Lucinda, Adam, Caz, Chrissie, Hana, Cat, Michelle and Robyn. A huge thank you to Jude who gave me excellent comments and suggestions early on, and to my former agent, Jill, for understanding that I just needed to write this book and not create other projects. I am so grateful for my editor, Susannah, who totally gets Bones and, along with the amazing team at Allen & Unwin, made this book come together (thank you!). Special thanks to my son, Calvin, and husband, Eric, who are mine and Sherlock Bones' biggest cheerleaders and supporters – I love you guys.

ABOUT THE AUTHOR

Renée first met Sherlock Bones shortly after arriving in
Australia in 2007. He was posing in an exhibit of tawny frogmouth
skeletons in the Queensland Museum in Brisbane. (In case you
are wondering, he was still there the last time she checked.)
The story came together years later after a visit to the
Melbourne Museum, which provided the perfect setting
and culprit. (And yes, he's still there too.)

Although Renée has been living in Australia for over ten years,
she is still fascinated by the wildlife and culture of this amazing
country. Her stories and illustrations are inspired by nature and
influenced by her background in environmental science. When
Renée is not writing or illustrating, she can be found walking
in the bush or on the beach, and exploring museums with her
family. She lives and works on the beautiful Surf Coast
in Victoria with her husband, son, and crazy little dog.